"Go and see what's on the TV," said Dad.
That made Jack feel very grumpy.

Jack pulled a grumpy face.

He flopped on to a chair in front of the TV.

"Grown-ups say such silly things,"
thought Jack. "I **know** what's on the TV –
there's a candlestick, there's a pot plant,
there's a photograph of Grandma."

Jack now felt really grumpy.

It was always grown-ups that made
him grumpy.

Jack sat and thought. He thought of all the silly things that grown-ups say.

When Mrs Brown from next door pops round, Mum says, "Oh, hello! I'll just put the kettle on."

Jack imagined Mum wearing a big kettle on her head. Just like a silly hat.

Jack smiled at the thought.

Jack thought about playing in Grandma's garden.

"Ooh, dear," says Grandma, "put your pullover on. You'll catch a chill."

She says it every time.

Jack wondered how fast a chill could run. Would he be able to catch it?

He grinned at the thought.

At school, Miss Henderson always says, "Come on, Jack! You haven't finished your work! Pull your socks up, boy!"

How do socks help you finish your work? Sometimes they haven't even fallen down.

Then Jack thought of his football landing in the flowerbed.

It always makes Dad cross.

"How many times have I told you not to do that?" says Dad.

Jack always replies that he hasn't been counting. That always seems to make Dad even more cross.

Sometimes Grandpa shouts at the people
on TV when he's watching the news.

"You can say **that** again!" shouts Grandpa.
They never do.

"Why is the tap running?" says Mum
whenever she goes in the bathroom.

Jack didn't even know it had legs.

"Can it run as fast as a chill?"
thought Jack.

The thought made him laugh out loud.
He forgot that he was feeling grumpy.

Dad heard the laughing and came in the room.

"You're happy!" he said.

"No, I'm Jack!" squeaked Jack, and he laughed and laughed even more.

Dad laughed too.

Then Mum called from the kitchen, "Dinner is on the table!"

Dad winked at Jack, "What! NO plates today then!" he said.

Jack and Dad laughed and laughed and laughed.

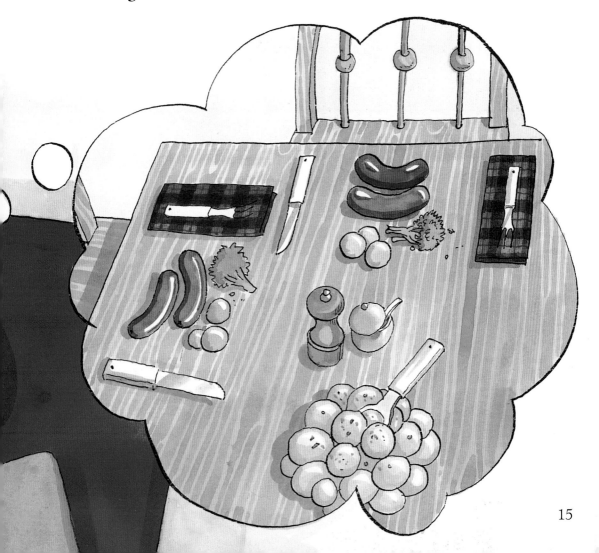

Mum came in.

Now **she** looked grumpy.

What are you two laughing at?